Food and Festivals

A Flavour of JAPAN

Teresa Fisher

HODDER
Wayland

Other titles:

Cover photograph:
A fish market in Tokyo.

Title page: A doll collection displayed for the Doll Festival.

Contents page: A girl praying at a Shinto shrine.

All Wayland books encourage children to read and help them improve their literacy.

✓ The contents page, page numbers, headings and index help locate specific pieces of information.

✓ The glossary reinforces alphabetic knowledge and extends vocabulary.

✓ The further information section suggests other books dealing with the same subject.

✓ Find out more about how this book is specifically relevant to the National Literacy Strategy on page 31.

First published in Great Britain in 1999 by Wayland Publishers Limited

First published in paperback in 2002 by Hodder Wayland, an imprint of Hodder Children's Books

© Hodder Wayland 1999

Hodder Children's Books
A division of Hodder Headline Limited
338 Euston Road, London NW1 3BH

Series editor: Polly Goodman
Book editor and picture researcher: Cath Senker
Cover picture research: Shelley Noronha
Designer: Tim Mayer

British Library Cataloguing in Publication Data
Fisher, Teresa
   A Flavour of Japan. – (Food and Festivals)
   1. Cookery, Japanese – Juvenile literature
   2. Food habits – Japan – Juvenile literature
   I. Title
   641.5'952
   ISBN 0 7502 4250 7

Typeset by Mayer Media
Printed and bound in Hong Kong

CONTENTS

Japan and its Food

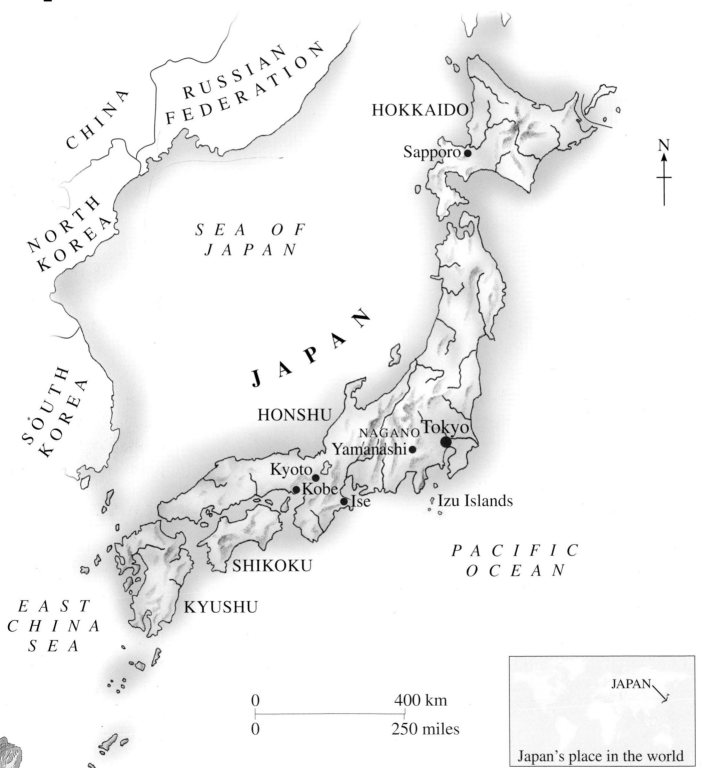

CHINA

RUSSIAN FEDERATION

HOKKAIDO

Sapporo ●

N

NORTH KOREA

SEA OF JAPAN

SOUTH KOREA

JAPAN

HONSHU

NAGANO
Yamanashi ●

Tokyo ●

Kyoto ●
● Kobe
● Ise

Izu Islands

PACIFIC OCEAN

EAST CHINA SEA

SHIKOKU

KYUSHU

0   400 km

0   250 miles

JAPAN

Japan's place in the world

4

RICE

Rice is one of the most important foods in Japan, eaten at every meal. There are many different rice dishes. Rice flour is used to make cakes and biscuits.

FISH

The Japanese eat more fish and seafood than any other people in the world. There are many different kinds of fish, including tuna, octopus and mackerel.

NOODLES

Noodles are Japan's most popular fast food. They are made from either wheat flour or buckwheat. Noodles are usually served in a bowl of hot fish broth with vegetables and eaten with chopsticks.

BEEF

Some of the most delicious beef in the world comes from Japan. In Kobe, beef is produced from cows that are kept underground, fed on beer and massaged each day. This makes the meat tender.

SOYA BEANS

Soya beans are very important in the Japanese diet. They are made into different kinds of food including beancurd, called *tofu*, and soya sauce.

SEAWEED

The Japanese love to eat seaweed. The main types are called *nori* (laver) and *kombu* (kelp). Seaweed is usually eaten with fish and tastes rather like salty spinach.

Food and Farming

▼ Winters are cold in the north of Japan. This spectacular ice festival is in Sapporo, Hokkaido.

Japan is a long, narrow country in the Pacific Ocean near China, Russia and Korea. It is made up of about 4,000 islands. The four largest islands are called Hokkaido, Honshu, Shikoku and Kyushu.

Since the land in Japan is very mountainous, most Japanese live near the sea in large, overcrowded cities. Thirteen million people live in Tokyo, the capital city.

There is little flat land suitable for farming. Every possible strip is used. In the countryside, the lower mountain slopes are terraced to make small level fields for growing cereals, fruit and vegetables.

In the city suburbs, sometimes you can see rice growing in small fields between the houses.

Houses in a village in ▶ Nagano, with small fields in between them.

▲ The rice is harvested in the autumn, often using machinery.

Farming

Japanese farmers produce three-quarters of the country's food. Rice is the main crop, grown on half the farmland. Growing rice is hard work, especially in springtime, when all the rice fields are flooded. Farmers have to work knee-deep in water to plant out the new rice shoots. Most farmers use machines to help them.

Fruit and vegetables are grown throughout Japan. Carrots, sweet potatoes, apples and pears are grown in the cool north. Tea, oranges, melons, peaches and tomatoes grow well in the south, where the climate is warmer.

FARMING FESTIVALS

Many of Japan's festivals are linked to important farming events. Each village has special celebrations when the rice is planted and harvested. One of the biggest is the Rice Planting Festival at Ise, with feasting, dancing and music.

▲ Fishermen sort the catch, ready for the daily fish market.

Fishing

Fishing is a major industry. Japan's fishing fleet is the biggest in the world. Fish such as tuna, cod, mackerel and sardines are caught. On land, there are special 'fish farms', producing eels, carp and rainbow trout. Seaweed is also grown for food.

Seaweed grown on the ▶ Izu Islands. Once gathered, the seaweed is left to dry in the sun.

◀ *Sushi*, made with rice and raw fish, is one of Japan's most popular dishes. You can see a pair of chopsticks and a bowl of soya sauce above the food.

Eating traditions

Traditional meals are always beautifully presented, with an enormous variety of dishes served in small portions. These are carefully arranged on plates and bowls of different colours and shapes. People eat with chopsticks, and traditionally sit cross-legged on a mat.

Today, however, Japanese people eat a lot of Western foods, such as hamburgers and pizzas. Fast-food restaurants are becoming more and more popular.

RICE

The Japanese eat rice at every meal. Even the words for breakfast, lunch and dinner in Japanese mean 'morning rice', 'noon rice' and 'evening rice'. Steamed rice is one of the most popular dishes, served in a small bowl. It is rather sticky, so it is easy to eat with chopsticks.

UNUSUAL DISHES

Some Japanese dishes are very unusual. Crunchy grasshoppers cooked in soya sauce and sugar, for example, are a popular snack. Another great delicacy is *sashimi* – bite-sized slices of different types of raw fish.

Japanese meals

A traditional breakfast in Japan is made up of rice, *miso* soup (a clear broth made from soya beans) and fish. Although most schools provide hot meals, many children take packed lunches to school. Dinner is the main meal, and a time for all the family to eat together.

▼ A family meal in Tokyo.

Shogatsu

The two main religions in Japan are Shintoism and Buddhism. Most people take part in both Buddhist and Shinto ceremonies and festivals. They believe that Shintoism affects their daily life and that Buddhism prepares them for life after death.

▼ This child at a Shinto shrine in Kyoto is ringing a bell to wake up the gods.

Shintoism

Followers of Shintoism believe that all natural things like the sun, trees and mountains are gods. Before praying at a Shinto shrine, they wash their hands. They then clap, and ring a bell to wake the gods.

There are many Shinto festivals for happy events such as harvests, births and marriages. *Shogatsu*, the New Year festival (on 1 January), is a Shinto celebration. It is the most important Japanese festival and most people stop work for several days to celebrate with their families.

▲ A girl prays at a shrine during an autumn Shinto festival in north Kyoto. Gifts of Japanese rice wine have been placed at the shrine.

The New Year festival

Preparations for the New Year festival begin early. People prepare special foods and buy gifts. Each house is decorated with a wreath of bamboo, pine and plum branches, and a rope of twisted straw. This is to keep away evil spirits.

Children always enjoy decorating the house with rice cakes. They also eat them hot, dipped in a sweet soya-bean powder, as a special treat.

A Shogatsu wreath ▶ of bamboo, pine and plum branches with twisted straw.

CHOPSTICKS

The Japanese have used chopsticks for eating food for hundreds of years. They are made of wood, bamboo or plastic, and come in different sizes and colours. Chopsticks are often beautifully decorated. Children learn to use them when they are very young, because good table manners are very important in Japan.

▲ This young boy has already learnt to use chopsticks to eat noodles.

On New Year's Eve, everyone eats noodles. Because noodles are long, people hope that eating them will give them long life. One popular dish is moon noodle soup – you can find out how to make it on page 17. After dinner, many families gather at the local shrine, where there is a massive bonfire. It burns all night.

15

New Year's Day

On New Year's Day, people eat special foods called *osechi-ryori* (pronounced 'oh-SAY-chi ree-OR-ee') from lacquered lunch boxes. These are carefully prepared the day before. The boxes have four layers, each containing a different course of the meal. Everyone sends New Year cards. It is a day for visiting friends and relatives, and playing traditional games. People enjoy street processions, parties and fireworks.

▲ Traditional New Year food, called *osechi-ryori*, in wooden lunch boxes.

ANIMAL OF THE YEAR

The years in Japan are named after twelve animals, including the dog, mouse, rat and tiger. At New Year, you can buy toy models of the 'animal of the year'.

◄ Moon noodle soup. Follow the recipe opposite to make it.

Moon Noodle Soup

EQUIPMENT

Measuring jug   Ladle

Saucepan   2 Soup bowls

Knife   Oven gloves

Chopping board

INGREDIENTS (for 2)

1 Stock cube (any kind)

450 ml Water

100 g Noodles (any kind)

2 Eggs

Bunch of spring onions, chopped into tiny pieces

1 Crumble the stock cube into the water and bring to the boil.

2 Cook the noodles in the stock, following the instructions on the packet of noodles.

3 Carefully break two eggs over the soup and cook for 5 minutes.

4 Sprinkle with spring onions and serve immediately.

Always be careful with boiling liquids. Ask an adult to help you.

Setsubun

Setsubun is the bean-throwing ceremony. This Shinto festival, on 3 or 4 February, celebrates the arrival of spring. Families decorate their homes and shrines with branches of the prickly *hiragi* tree (which is like the holly tree). They hang sardine heads in the doorways for luck.

▲ Sumo wrestlers at a bean-throwing ceremony at a temple.

People then scatter roasted soya beans in and around the house to drive away sickness, bad luck and demons. As they throw the beans, they shout *Fuku-wa-uchi, oni-wa-soto* (In with good fortune, out with devils).

Soya beans are also eaten. It is considered lucky to eat a bean for every year of your age.

CEREMONIES AT SHRINES

Soya beans are not only scattered around the home. Special bean-throwing ceremonies take place at local shrines too. These are led by a well-known sportsperson, television star or other famous person. Catching one of their beans is thought to be especially lucky.

▲ Children in Yamanashi wearing demon masks and trying to catch soya beans.

Children especially enjoy *Setsubun* because they dress up in demon masks and have great fun throwing beans at each other. If you catch one, you are supposed to have good luck for the rest of the year.

Although there are no special set meals for *Setsubun*, most families eat food made from soya beans, including *miso* soup and *tofu* dishes. One especially tasty soya-bean dish is *miso*-topped beancurd. There's a recipe for this dish on the opposite page. Bean-paste sweets are also great favourites.

▲ *Miso*-topped beancurd. The recipe for this dish is on the opposite page.

Bean-paste sweets. ▶ The bean paste is made from soya beans.

Miso-topped Beancurd

EQUIPMENT

Knife   Oven gloves
Chopping board   Spatula
Grill pan   Large plate

INGREDIENTS (for 4)

1 Block of *tofu* (beancurd)
100 g Red *miso* paste

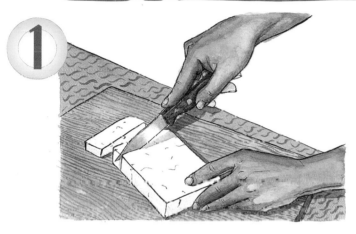

Cut the *tofu* into pieces about 5 cm long and 2 cm wide.

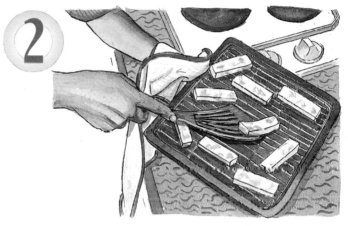

Ask an adult to grill the pieces until they are lightly browned on both sides.

Allow the *tofu* to cool for a minute. Spread each piece with the red *miso* paste.

Return to the grill until the *tofu* turns a reddish-brown colour.
Serve immediately.

Always be careful when using the grill. Ask an adult to help you.

Children's Festivals

▼ Girls wearing *kimonos* sit with a doll collection for *Hina Matsuri*.

Children's festivals in Japan come from ancient Shinto traditions.

Hina Matsuri

The third day of the third month (3 March) marks *Hina Matsuri*, the Doll Festival. It is a special day for girls, who dress up in *kimonos* and show off their best dolls. Then they visit their friends' houses to admire their doll collections.

The dolls are offered a sweet rice drink called *amazake* (pronounced 'a-ma-ZA-ki') and coloured rice cakes, which the family eats afterwards.

These are carp ▶ streamers. The red carp is for the youngest boy in the family. Green and blue carp are for the older boys. The black carp is for the father.

Kodomo-no-hi

Kodomo-no-hi, or Children's Day, is a national holiday that takes place on 5 May. It is mainly to celebrate the energy and ambition of boys. Boys hang giant, brightly coloured streamers in the shape of carp fish out of the window.

The family eats special foods, including white rice dumplings filled with sweet red-bean paste. Red and white are the traditional colours for celebration food. There are always plenty of red and white rice and fish dishes. Treats for dessert are rice cakes and orange baskets. There's a recipe for orange baskets on page 25.

▲ Orange baskets.

Shichi-go-san

Shichi-go-san, or Seven-Five-Three Day, is on 15 November. It is for girls who are seven or three years old, and boys who are five or three. The children dress up in their best clothes and go with their families to the local shrine. They pray for good health and a long life.

The children tie prayers to the branches of trees, or pin them to the shrines. Then they are given bags of red and white sweets, which are said to bring 'a thousand years of happiness' to those who eat them.

◀ A family celebrating *Shichi-go-san* at a Shinto shrine in Tokyo.

Orange Baskets

Ask an adult to cut off the top quarter of each orange and slice off the ends so they stand upright. Now cut a zigzag shape around the top.

Scoop out the orange flesh with the grapefruit knife and spoon and cut into bite-sized pieces. Cut each grape in half lengthways.

Fill the orange skins with the grape and orange pieces.

Cover the orange baskets with cling film and put them in the fridge for at least 30 minutes before serving.

Take care when using knives. Ask an adult to help you.

Obon Festival

Japan's second most important festival, *Obon*, takes place on 15 July in cities and 15 August in the countryside. It is a Buddhist festival in honour of relatives who have died. *Obon* is the time when it is believed they come back to Earth. Families visit the relatives' graves and shrines to decorate them with flowers and burn incense.

▲ A family visiting a grave for the *Obon* festival.

BUDDHISM

Buddhism is based on the teachings of a holy man called the Buddha. Japanese Buddhists believe that if they follow Buddhist teachings they will be prepared for death and looked after once they are dead. Every temple contains a statue of the Buddha. The largest one is taller than a three-storey building, and can be seen in the temple at Nara.

A statue of the ▶ Buddha in Tokyo.

In the evening, lanterns are lit outside houses to help the dead find their way back home. There is dancing and a great feast of favourite summer dishes. These include *sushi*, summer salads and beef *teriyaki* (chunks of steak in a sticky, dark-brown sauce).

For dessert, people like to eat green tea ice-cream and cold savoury custards. You can find out how to make savoury custards on page 29.

Green tea ice-cream. ▶

At the end of the night, a special dance called the *Bon-Odori* is performed in the grounds of the temples. People dance to the music of the *shamisen*, a traditional Japanese musical instrument. The *Bon-Odori* is believed to send the spirits back after their visit home.

▲ Cold savoury custard. There's a recipe for this dish on the opposite page.

▼ These women and children are dancing the *Bon-Odori*.

Cold Savoury Custards

EQUIPMENT

Measuring jug
Tablespoon
4 Small bowls
Kitchen foil

Saucepan and steamer
Oven gloves
Grater
Plate

INGREDIENTS (for 4)

4 Eggs
200 ml *Dashi* (Japanese fish and seaweed stock) – or a stock cube (ideally fish) with 200 ml water
1 Tablespoon light soya sauce
Pinch of sugar
4 Shrimps or prawns
Grated orange or lemon peel

1 Mix the eggs, *dashi*, soy sauce and sugar in the jug. Pour into the bowls and cover each one with foil. Half-fill the saucepan with boiling water.

2 Put the bowls in the steamer, and the steamer in the saucepan. Put on the lid and steam for about 20 minutes (or until the eggs have set).

3 Carefully lift the bowls out of the steamer. Let the custards cool, then put them in the fridge until they are chilled.

4 Before serving, place a shrimp on top of each and decorate with grated orange or lemon peel.

Always be careful with boiling liquids. Ask an adult to help you with the steamer.

Glossary

Beancurd A solid food, often called *tofu*, which is made from soya milk and sold in blocks. It looks a bit like crumbly cheese.

Broth A thin soup made with fish or meat stock.

Buddhism One of the main religions of Japan, based on the teachings of a holy man called the Buddha.

Chopsticks A pair of sticks, usually made of wood, plastic or bamboo, used for eating in Japan and other nearby countries.

Delicacy A type of food that is considered very special and delicious.

Incense A mixture of herbs and spices shaped into thin sticks. They make a sweet-smelling smoke when burned.

Kimono A traditional loose-fitting robe worn by both men and women.

Lacquered Covered in a tough varnish, called 'lacquer'. Lacquered items are very popular in Japan.

Miso A strong-tasting paste made from soya beans, frequently used in Japanese cooking.

Shinto One of the main religions of Japan, and the oldest. It is based on the worship of ancestors and the spirits of nature.

Shrine A small place where gods and goddesses are worshipped. Shinto celebrations take place at shrines.

Temple A place where gods are worshipped. Buddhists worship at temples.

Terraced land A series of flat areas cut into a hillside so that crops can be grown there.

Photograph and artwork acknowledgements
The publishers would like to thank the following for allowing their pictures to be used in this book:
Axiom (all Jim Holmes) 5 (middle right), 7, 15, 20 (below); Steve Benbow 11; Britstock-IFA (HAGA) *title page*, 6, 14, 16 (above), 19, 22, 24; Cephas (TOP/Bernhard Winkelman) 27; Chapel Studios (Zul Mukhida) 10, 16 (below), 20 (above) and 23 (below), (Tim Garrod) 23 (above), (Zul Mukhida) 28 (above); Eye Ubiquitous (John Dakers) 9 (below), 18, (John Dakers) 28 (below); Robert Harding 26 (above); Frank Leather *cover photo*, *contents page*, 12, 13; Panos Pictures (Jim Holmes) 5 (top right); TRIP (A. Tovy) 26 (below); Wayland Picture Library 8, 9 (above).

Fruit and vegetable artwork is by Tina Barber. The map artwork on page 4 is by Peter Bull and Hardlines.
The step-by-step recipe artwork is by Judy Stevens.

Topic Web and Resources

MATHS

Use and understand data and measures (recipes).

Use and read measuring instruments: scales.

Use weights and measures.

Use and understand fractions.

SCIENCE

Food and nutrition.

Health.

Plants in different habitats.

Mixing and dissolving different materials.

Changing materials through heat.

GEOGRAPHY

Locality study.

Landscapes and climate.

Farming and how land is used.

Influence of landscape on human activities: where people live, farming and food festivals.

DESIGN AND TECHNOLOGY

Make a carp streamer.

Design a *kimono*.

Decorate chopstick handles.

Food & Festivals
TOPIC WEB

HISTORY

Japanese traditions.

MODERN FOREIGN LANGUAGES

Everyday activities: food.

People, places and customs.

Language skills: learn a few phrases in Japanese.

MUSIC

Listen to Japanese music.

Find out about Japanese instruments used at festivals.

ENGLISH

Write a poem or a story about a Japanese festival.

Describe some Japanese dishes.

R.E.

Food and festivals.

Buddhism and Shinto.

OTHER BOOKS TO READ

A First Guide to Japan by Kath Davies (Zoë Books, 1995)

Country Fact Files: Japan by John Baines (Macdonald Young Books, 1997)

Country Insights: Japan by Nick Bornoff (Wayland, 1996)

The Food of Japan by Wendy Hutton (Periplus World Cookbooks, 1995)

We Come from Japan by Teresa Fisher (Wayland, 1998)

USEFUL ADDRESSES

Japan Festival Education Trust: Swire House, 59 Buckingham Gate, London SW1E 6AJ. Tel: 0207 630 8696.

Japanese Information Culture Centre: Embassy of Japan, 101 Piccadilly, London W1V 9FN. Tel: 0207 465 6500.

Japanese National Tourist Organisation: 20 Savile Row, London SW1X 1AE. Tel: 0207 734 9638.

This book meets the following specific objectives of the National Literacy Strategy's Framework for Teaching:

✓ Range of work in non-fiction: simple recipes (especially Year 2, Term 1), instructions, labels, captions, lists, glossary, index.

✓ Vocabulary extension: words linked to particular topics (food words) and technical words from work in other subjects (geography and food science).

GAME

Multicultural Food Fun (NES Arnold, Nottingham) Young children can match food to the country of origin.

Index

Page numbers in **bold** mean there is a photograph on the page.